EDUCATIONAL

Back to Basics

MATHS

for 5-6 year olds

BOOK TWO

George Rodda

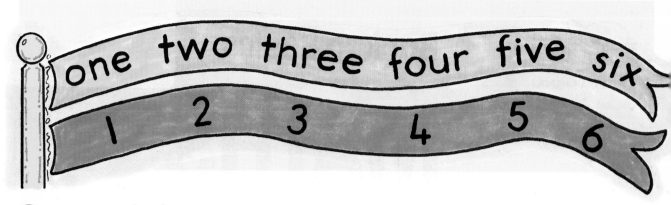

one two three four five six

1   2   3   4   5   6

Count how many

4 flags

four flags

☐ shells

☐☐☐ shells

☐ spades

☐☐ spades

☐ crabs

☐☐ crabs

4 boats

Count how many

☐ red boats

☐ blue boats

☐ fish

☐ rods

Draw
6 boats and 2 fish

3

7   8
seven eight

7 7 7 7 7 7 7

seven seven seven

8 8 8 8 8 8 8

eight eight eight

Count how many

☐ cats

☐ dogs

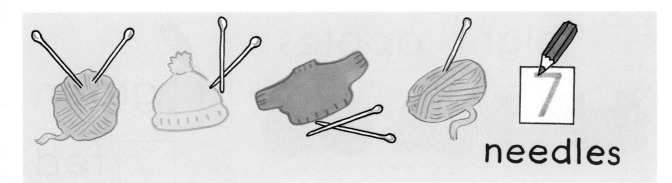

Count how many

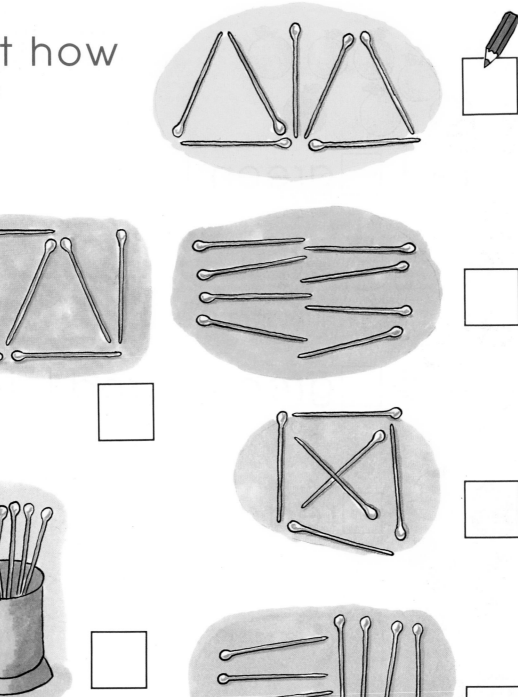

eight apples

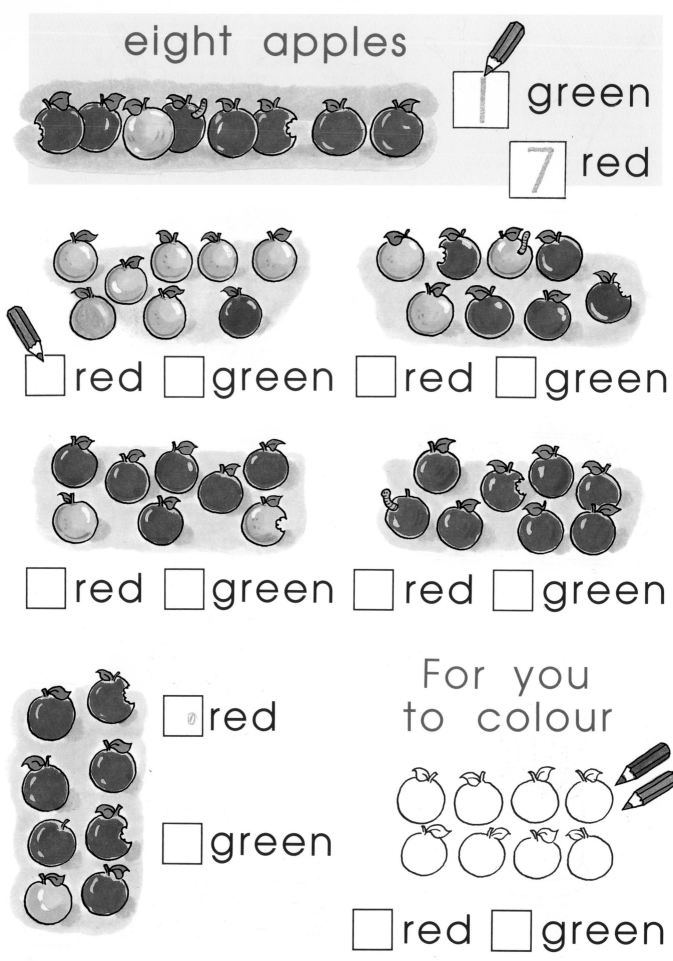

green
1

red
7

☐ red ☐ green

☐ red ☐ green

☐ red ☐ green

☐ red ☐ green

☐ red

☐ green

For you
to colour

☐ red ☐ green

6

9 nine

10 ten

9 9 9 9 9 9 9

nine nine nine nine

10 10 10 10 10 10 10

ten ten ten ten

Count how many

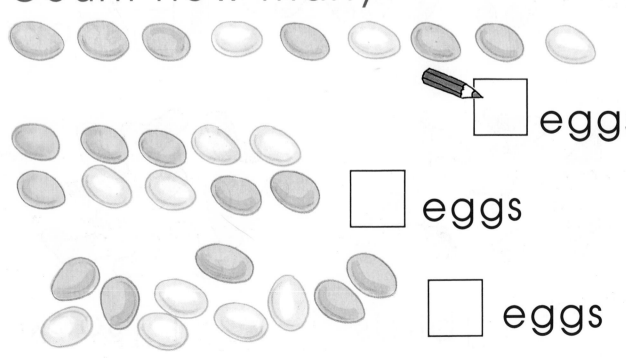

☐ eggs

☐ eggs

☐ eggs

socks and birds

Count how many

 birds

☐ socks

☐ birds

☐ socks

 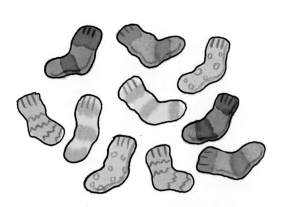

☐ birds ☐ socks

add = 5 birds

4 add 1 = ☐

4 add 2 = ☐

4 add 3 = ☐

5 add 1 = ☐   5 add 2 = ☐

6 add 1 = ☐   7 add 1 = ☐

6 add 3 = ☐   7 add 2 = ☐

8 add 1 = ☐   8 add 2 = ☐

9 add 1 = ☐   5 add 5 = ☐

5 sheep + 3 sheep = 8 sheep

+ = ☐ sheep

4 + 3 = ☐   3 + 4 = ☐

+ = ☐ sheep

6 + 3 = ☐   3 + 6 = ☐

+ = ☐ sheep

5 + 4 = ☐   4 + 5 = ☐

5 + 0 = ☐   5 + 5 = ☐

Patterns

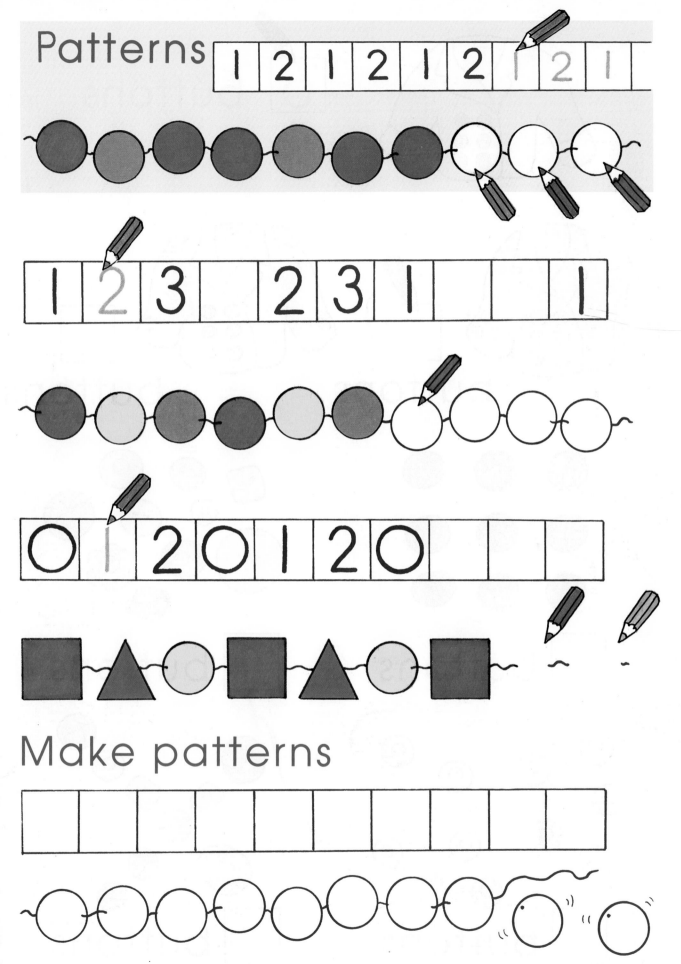

| 1 | 2 | 1 | 2 | 1 | 2 | 1 | 2 | 1 |

| 1 | 2 | 3 | | 2 | 3 | 1 | | 1 |

| O | 1 | 2 | O | 1 | 2 | O | | | |

Make patterns

11

  **6** buttons

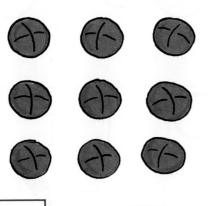  buttons

 buttons

 buttons

 buttons

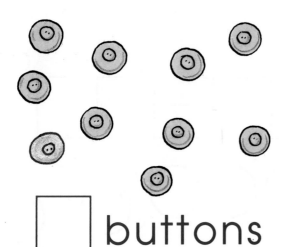 buttons

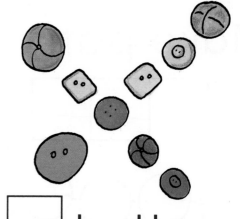 buttons

Draw the buttons

 +  = 10 buttons

 + = 10 buttons

8 + ☐ = 10

+ = 10 buttons

9 + ☐ = 10

+ = 10 buttons

7 + ☐ = 10

6 + ☐ = 10   5 + ☐ = 10

Corners

Little Jack Horner sat in a corner

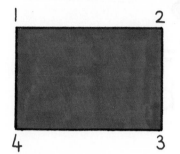

This shape has  4 corners

Colour shapes

4 corners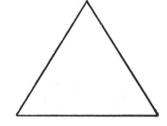
3 corners
0 corners

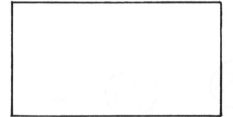

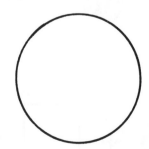

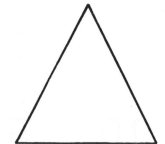

This shape
has 5 corners

red   blue   green   yellow

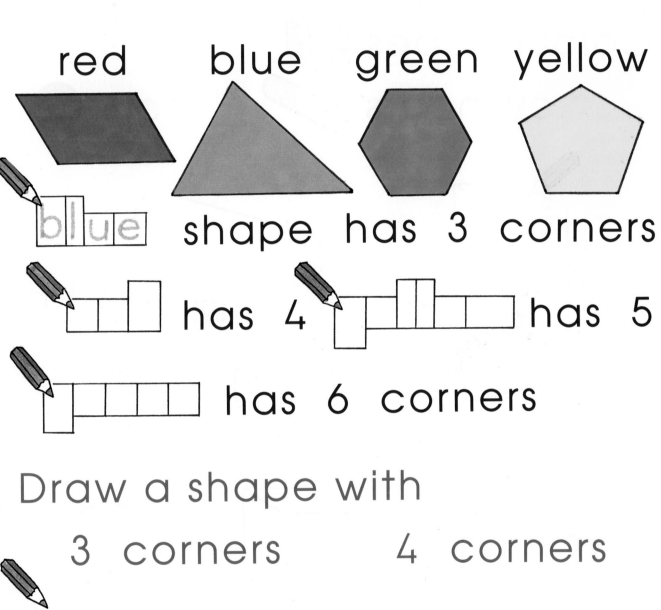

blue shape has 3 corners

has 4   has 5

has 6 corners

Draw a shape with

3 corners   4 corners

Cube

Cylinder

Ball

Colour cubes

cylinders

balls

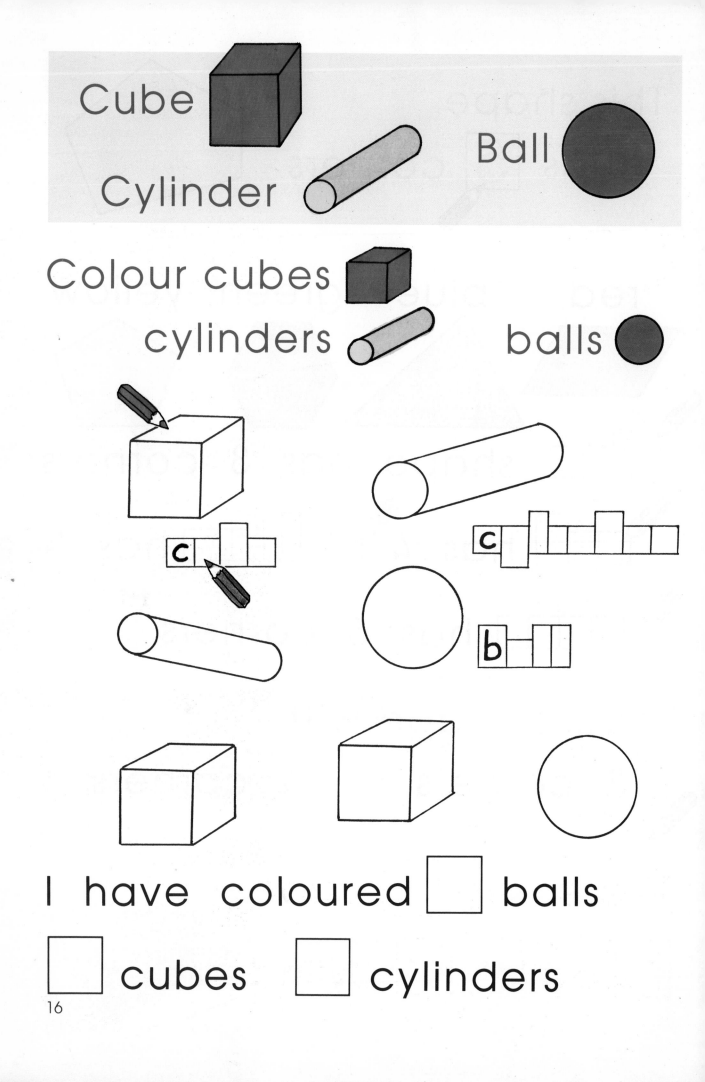

c

c

b

I have coloured ☐ balls

☐ cubes   ☐ cylinders

16

Shapes

Match the shapes

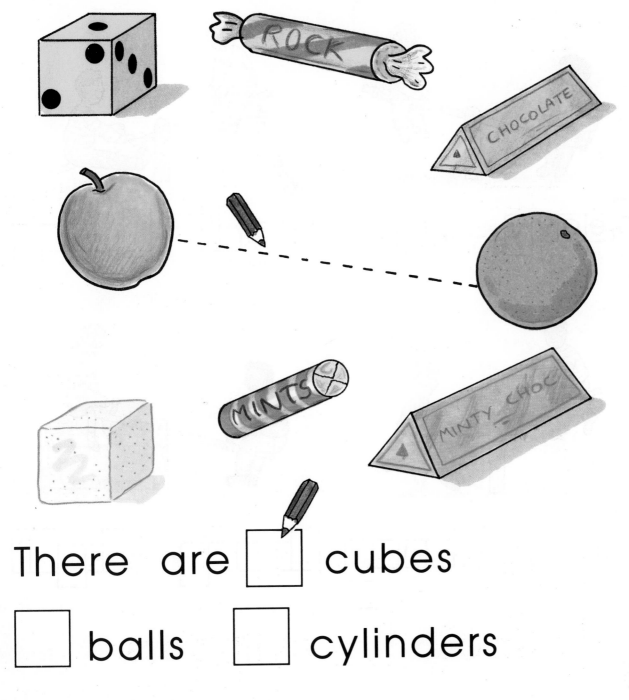

There are ☐ cubes

☐ balls   ☐ cylinders

17

heavy   light   light   heavy

Colour large red   small blue

large   small   small   large

19

$$(2p) + (1p) + (1p) = \boxed{4}\ p$$

$$(1p) + (1p) + (1p) = \boxed{}\ p$$

$$(1p) + (1p) + (2p) = \boxed{}\ p$$

$$(1p) + (2p) + (2p) = \boxed{}\ p$$

$$(2p) + (2p) + (2p) = \boxed{}\ p$$

$$(5p) + (1p) + (1p) = \boxed{}\ p$$

$$(5p) + (2p) + (1p) = \boxed{}\ p$$

$$(5p) + (2p) + (2p) = \boxed{}\ p$$

$$(5p) + (1p) + (2p) = \boxed{}\ p$$

$$(1p) + (2p) + (5p) = \boxed{}\ p$$

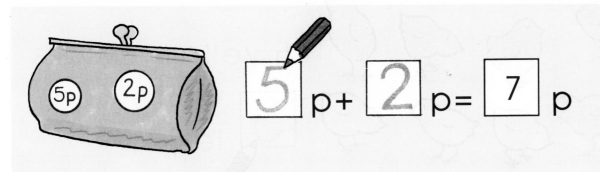

5 p $+$ 2 p $=$ 7 p

☐ p $+$ ☐ p $=$ 4 p

☐ p $+$ ☐ p $+$ ☐ p $=$ ☐ p

☐ p $+$ ☐ p $+$ ☐ p $=$ ☐ p

☐ p $+$ ☐ p $+$ ☐ p $=$ ☐ p

☐ p $+$ ☐ p $=$ ☐ p

☐ p $+$ ☐ p $=$ ☐ p

5 yellow chicks

3 white ones left

☐ yellow chicks

☐ white ones left

Colour 6 chicks

☐ white ones left

Colour 6 chicks

☐ white ones left

☐ chicks colour 6

☐ white chicks left

22

Cover 6

4 left

Cover 4

☐ left

Cover 3

☐ left

Cover 7

☐ left

Cover 1

☐ left

23

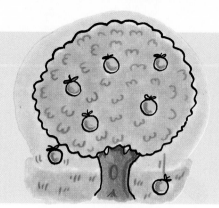

7 apples on the tree
2 fall off
$7 - 2 = 5$ left

7 apples
eat 3

4 left

$7 - 3 = \boxed{}$

$7 - 4 = \boxed{}$ $7 - 5 = \boxed{}$

$\boxed{}$ apples eat 3

$\boxed{}$ left

$6 - 3 = \boxed{}$

$6 - 4 = \boxed{}$ $6 - 6 = \boxed{}$

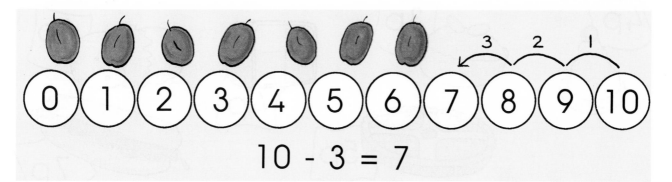

$$10 - 3 = 7$$

How many plums?

1 falls off ☐ left

10 - 1 = ☐

10 - 2 = ☐   10 - 4 = ☐

How many plums? ☐

eat 7 ☐ left

8 - 7 = ☐

8 - 6 = ☐   8 - 5 = ☐

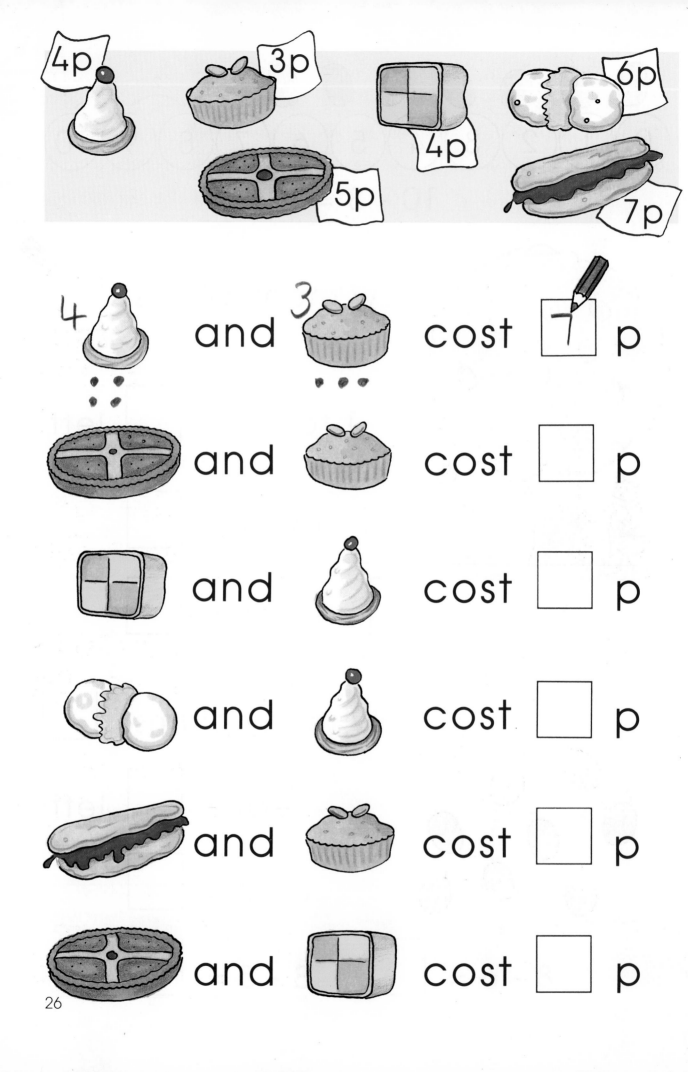

4 🔔 and 3 🧁 cost 7 p

🥧 and 🧁 cost ☐ p

⬜ and 🔔 cost ☐ p

🍞 and 🔔 cost ☐ p

🥖 and 🧁 cost ☐ p

🥧 and ⬜ cost ☐ p

10p - $\boxed{6p}$ = $\boxed{4}$ p
change
from 10p

$\boxed{}$ p
change
from 10p

$\boxed{}$ p
change
from 10p

$\boxed{}$ p
change
from 10p

$\boxed{}$ p
change
from 10p

and $\boxed{}$ p change from 10p

and $\boxed{}$ p change from 10p

and $\boxed{}$ p change from 10p

 **Time**  The clock wakes me at 7 o'clock

  **9** o'clock

  **3** o'clock

 ☐ o'clock

 ☐ o'clock

 ☐ o'clock

 ☐ o'clock

 ☐ o'clock go to bed

Monday is a school day

Sunday
Monday
Tuesday
Wednesday
Thursday
Friday
Saturday

number

My school days are
  Monday number **2**

number

number

number

number

I go to school for ☐ days

1 week is ☐ days

Ten
green
bottles

ten ☐ bottles

nine ☐ bottles

eight ☐ bottles

seve_ ☐ bottles

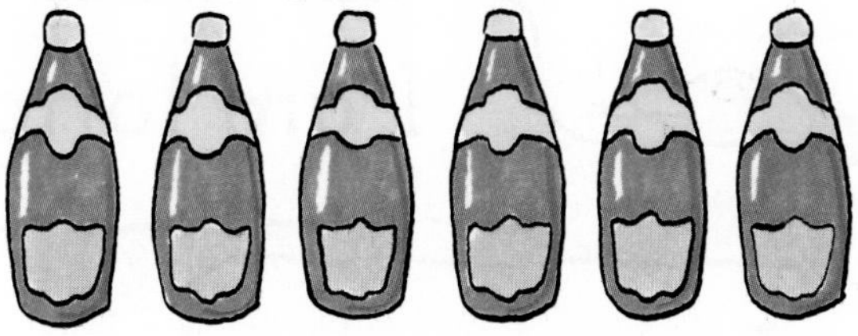

si_ ☐ bottles

fiv_ ☐ bottles

fou_ ☐ bottles

thre_ ☐ bottles

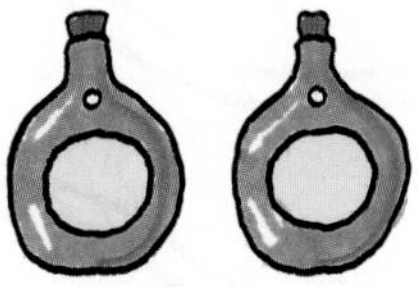

tw_ ☐ bottles

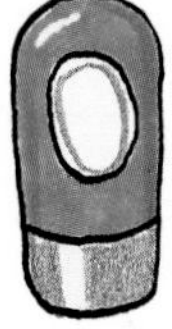

o_ _ ☐ bottles

no bottles left

Colour the longest one yellow
the shortest one green

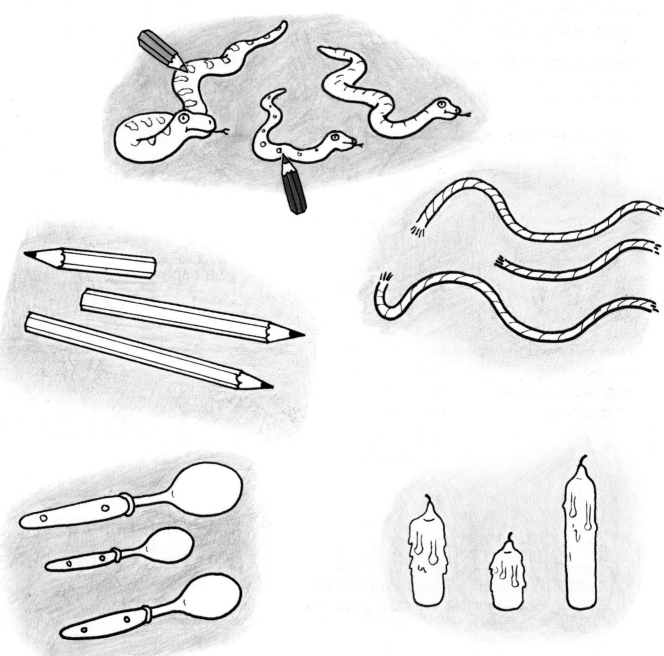